# Gone For Good

## Tales from a Bristol Boyhood

# Gone For Good

## Tales from a Bristol Boyhood

Lewis Wilshire

REDCLIFFE
Bristol

Dedication:
To Radio Bristol in general, and
Pete Lawrence in particular

*First published 1985 by
Redcliffe Press Ltd.,
49 Park Street, Bristol BS1 5NT*

ISBN 0 905459 67 9

Typeset by Folio Photosetting, Bristol
Printed by Photobooks, Bristol

# Contents

# Gone for Good

When winter comes, and the wind is lashing rain against the windowpane and howling in the chimney, most of us like to draw the curtains and shut out the weather.

At times like this, when sensible folk like you and I take cover and let the elements fight it out, Old Solly would be up and about – cleaning the drains, unblocking watercourses, directing the traffic round fallen trees. He seemed to think it was his special responsibility to cope with wind and storm.

Not that he was paid to do it. His real job was a watchman – a nightwatchman – it was just that bad weather excited him, like a leech in a bottle.

Where there were roadworks you'd find him, lording it over his oil-lamps and equipment – all the picks and shovels – grouped around the Monster, a magnificent steam-roller. But for Solly, small boys might have swarmed all over it, turning wheels and mucking about with brakes. That would have been desecration. Because steam-rollers were sacred objects – the storm-centre of roadworks – only to be contemplated from a distance –with awe.

It's all different, now – just a line of automatic-flashing lights and a hole in the road. No equipment, no steam-roller – and above all, no nightwatchman. But in those days, the watchman's hut, with its brazier of glowing coke, was a friendly sight. If he happened to be frying-up or baking potatoes in his brazier, he would have plenty of company. A couple of small boys, a friend who wanted a yarn, or a tramp who was good company. Of course, some of them didn't encourage company, but Solly did. He knew all the regular tramps, and loved telling the tales. It's difficult to convey the excitement, because the magic of being out after dark vanished with the gas-lamps. In these days of stark electric-light, it's not the same at all.

Solly had been a seaman in his youth, and he liked to play the part of the Ancient Mariner, recounting storms at sea and shipwrecks. He would show us his tattoos, one on each arm and a magnificent steamer in the sunset on his chest, to illustrate the tales. According to him, he had a masterpiece, lower down, but he couldn't show us that – it was for his eyes only!

One of the most popular of his stories – and certainly, the one he was fondest of telling – was about a shipwreck. It happened at the mouth of the Conger – must have been the Congo, but he was a local man – and it involved a typhoon. If you'd never seen one, Solly said, you'd never seen Nature at its greatest. It was as if sea and sky were one – sea below and sea above, waves like hills, and troughs like valleys, whirlwinds and whirlpools, howling gales and thunder-and-lightning.

You got the impression that to live through a typhoon made a man of you or drowned you. Solly – needless to say – had come through.

His ship hadn't. She had floundered about in the tempest, her engines had failed, and two crewmen and the mate were washed overboard. The Captain locked himself in his cabin and got drunk, and it was all hands to the pumps to keep the ship afloat.

"We pumped and pumped till we couldn' pump no more," he said. "Just dropped down, exhausted, we did, past caring whether we lived or died."

At this point, the narrative became somewhat confused. Solly would get excited in the telling of it, and his teeth – which weren't much of a fit – would clatter like castanets. They'd slip, and he'd have to adjust them, and you lost some of the story.

It seemed as though the ship was washed on to some rocks. And the crew were so tired and apathetic, by that time, that they lay there and waited to drown, too weak to care.

They must have slept, and the storm abated. Next morning, he was awakened by a hand on his shoulder. At first, he couldn't believe he was still in the land of the living. The sea was calm as a millpond, the ship stuck firm on these rocks, and only the two of them, he and Parno, his shipmate, left alive.

Whilst they were still sitting there, dazed with the shock of being alive, two or three canoes set out from shore and paddled around the ship. They didn't know whether they would be saved or attacked, but they weren't in much of a bargaining position. The natives were suspicious of them, and they were wary of the natives, but despite the fact that neither knew the others' language, they did a deal.

All the cargo and fittings were stripped from the ship, and Parno and Solly went to live in the native-village. Solly would tell us about the mud-huts and the jungle, but there were some things he wouldn't tell us.

Were they cannibals, for instance? He didn't

know. They had some funny customs, he said, but it wasn't his business.

"What happened to the Captain?" we asked. Solly said he'd knocked his head when the ship struck, and by the time they broke open his cabin door, he was dead. Then Parno had been taken off with a fever, and he – Solly – became one of the tribe.

"Not a bad life," he said, "if you don't mind roughing it."

At this point, he would look moodily at the listeners, spit in the fire, and add: "And then they bloody well come and rescued me!"

The trouble was, when the rescuers found the hulk stripped and Solly alone alive to tell the tale, they arrested him, and took him back to civilization. We gathered that that was like going into prison, maybe a prison sentence did follow. Anyway, Solly's enthusiasm always evaporated when the moment of rescue came.

"Oh well," he'd say, "that was a long time ago. Spect the old tub's broken-up by this time. Nothing left, 'cept me . . . Now, come on, you boys. There's a storm brewing up, or I'm a Dutchman – better be away off home!"

He'd cock an eye at the moon, with clouds scudding across its face, and light his pipe from an ember. He must have had hands like leather, because he could pick up an ember from the brazier, as though it weren't hot at all. It must have been the speed, I suppose. Whatever it was, he had the knack . . .

And as I say, he was at his best in time of storm and tempest. When the lightning danced and the street-lamps flickered, he would come alive.

"Things is livening up," he'd say. "We'm in for a beauty, I'd say."

Did I say you don't meet characters like Solly any more? Some enthusiasts of the age of steam have done up old steam-rollers. Shone their brass and oiled their wheels. Made 'em look a picture. But there's no preserving human beings. You can't clean *them* up. They're gone for good!

———————

# Uncle George
# and the Golden Railing

My Gran's brother George was not completely blind. People said he was, but it was belied by the fact that he wore thick-lensed spectacles. So thick, indeed, and so great the magnification that his eyes looked like tadpoles in a goldfish-bowl. It was curious – and rather frightening.

According to Uncle George, he could just see the difference between light and dark. And if he held a newspaper four inches in front of him, he could just discern the headlines by squinting at them sideways.

Not that he was a misery, mind you, Uncle George was ever-cheerful, a notorious gossip, and a businessman. True, it wasn't a big business, and if he hadn't had a blind pension, things would have gone hard for them, he and Aunt Annie, in their terraced Victorian villa next to the Plymouth Brethren, at Staple Hill.

Although Aunt Annie sold sweets in the front-room of their house, it wasn't exactly a shop. And indeed, that part of the business was non-profitmaking. No. His business was conducted on foot. He sold tea.

It was all a bit mysterious. He had once had an agency for cutlery. A firm called Fattorini, at Sheffield, supplied the goods, and he sold them on a never-never basis. On tick.

But that didn't prosper, so he switched to tea.

People needed supplies weekly, and unlike cutlery, it was a consumer product. In our locality you required six knives, forks and spoons, a carving-knife and some tablespoons, and that was it. They passed, in due course, to children, and I'll say this for Fattorinis – their products wore well. So Uncle George switched to tea, which had an Indian-sounding name and was not much inferior to the better-known brands. In fact, Uncle George claimed it was vastly superior.

My impression of Uncle George, now, is dominated by those thick glasses and a heavy double-looped watch-chain, which dropped imposing across a snuff-coloured waistcoat, passing through a buttonhole, securing a golden sovereign with a hole in it in his right-hand pocket and an enormous pocket-watch in his left. This watch was a marvel. Nickel-plated and built to last, it had a ponderous solemnity which suited him.

He used to produce it, with a flourish, for examination: flicking open the shield which protected the glass-face with the nail of his thumb. Its face was like Big Ben in miniature, but that was unimportant compared with its chime, for it was a blind-man's watch – press down the winder, and it chimed the nearest hour. You didn't even have to open it to discover the hour, but Uncle George liked to demonstrate all its faculties.

There were people who said (not to his face) that the tea-business was a cover; that Uncle George took betting-slips as well. But I don't know . . . He certainly covered a lot of ground, and as he had always lived in the same place, he knew every road, lane and stile for miles. Sight didn't seem important to him, and I've watched him crossing roads, opening gates, whistling tonelessly and stopping to take a pinch of snuff or exchange the time of day, as though he could see as well as you or I.

They say that if you lose one sense, nature compensates by improving another. That was true of Uncle George: he could hear a pin drop. Stopping to cross a road, he would listen for traffic or footsteps, and was afraid only of cyclists, and alterations. Any sort of alteration in his territory brought a crisis, because he had adapted to it, could move about it in safety, provided it stayed the same.

Strangely, his wife Annie depended on him. He was the strong one of the partnership. They had no children. And he said, didn't need any. Annie was his child. He doted on her, spoilt her, and she accepted his infatuation as a natural right.

In her youth, Aunt Annie had been pretty, and she kept her looks because she never really grew up. She was a fluttery, sentimental, simple sort of person with a fondness for sweets, an inability to cook and unable to understand the simplest arithmetical problem. Uncle George was no scholar, but he was one of those men who, without any formal education could work out complicated sums in his head, like a mini-computer.

It was Uncle George who did the shopping, delivered the tea, collected the pension, and exchanged gossip at the barber's. Aunt Annie stayed at home, selling sweets in the front-room and sampling far too many in between customers. If the children who were her customers were crafty enough, they would engage her in conversation, she would forget that they hadn't paid for their purchases, and Uncle George would tell her, once again, to keep her mind on the job.

As a sweet shop it was hopeless, but then, it kept her happy, and Uncle George accepted their stock-losses philosophically.

"She got her good points," he'd say, implying that they had to be paid for.

"Doesn't he *mind* being blind?" I asked my Gran, his elder sister.

"He's got used to it", she said, stitching away in the light of her Aladdin lamp. "It kept him out of the war, and brings him a pension, and people feel sorry for 'n. It don't seem to stop him doing much, do it?"

I had to admit that it didn't.

He had not always, she said, been so near-sighted. Although he had had glasses from childhood, his sight had worsened as he grew older, and he had had time to adapt to it. Annie had been one of the prettiest girls in the parish when he married her, and he had not seen her lose her figure and her looks. To him, she was still the fresh young girl he had made a home for, and he treated her with a playful coyness that other people found embarrassing or touching.

To me, a cynical little boy of ten, it was just plain silly. She would flutter around him, giggling, whilst he would become the young lover again, archly superior, telling her to behave herself. What a mixture, I told myself, he blind and she daft.

Their house was just an ordinary terraced villa, but it had tall, iron railings. Like a row of spears, joined together by horizontal strips. I had this compulsion, always, when passing their house, to run my right-forefinger along the spear-heads, taking care not to miss one out. And that was how I made the discovery, an event which was to change my life.

One day, in running my finger along the spears,

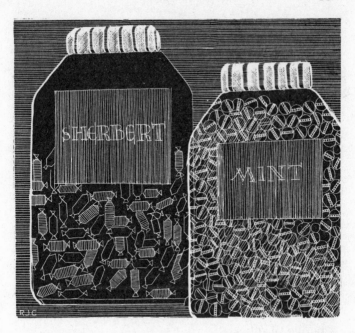

I discovered that one of them was loose. You could move it about in its socket. I pulled it, and felt it rise. Feeling like young Arthur pulling the sword from the stone, I held my breath and pulled hard. It came away in my hand. The ornamental head capped an iron shaft about four feet long. I waited until the coast was clear, and ran home with it, carrying it like a talisman, unable to believe my good luck.

My old man had bought some gilt paint and was doing-up two picture-frames. I used it on my spear, and the result was exhilarating.

*Give me my bow*, we sang, lustily at school prayers, *of burning gold, give me my arrows of desire*. Well, this was the same sort of thing – a golden spear – my prayers were answered.

Fortunate for me, I thought, Uncle George was too blind to notice it was missing and Aunt Annie too daft. I took it with me when our gang met at our secret *rendezvous* behind Buller Howe's cart-shed.

"Whassat?" asked Shirty, so-called because he had never been seen without his shirt-tail flapping.

"I found it," I said, "fixed to a stone."

"Let's see," the other three asked, but the spear had given me a new authority, I wouldn't let them hold it. "It can only be held by me," I said. "You'd get a 'lectric shock."

This was sensational. Overnight I became leader. The golden spear was a symbol. It eclipsed the wonder of Don Gibson's invention of tying stinging-nettles to bean-poles for lances in our wars with the Gorse Hill gang. It took precedence over the old car without wheels in Dennis's yard, and I carried it before me like a badge of office.

Our ritual enemies recoiled from this new magic. I was a boy to be noticed, now, it added about three feet to my stature, and but for Uncle George I might have remained a leader the rest of my life.

It was he, of course, who discovered its loss. His white-stick which ran before him, always, like a prehensible, exploring finger found it missing, and he knew that the culprit could only be a boy.

"Some boy must've taken it, Sarah," he told my Gran. "I knew he was loose, and I meant to cement 'n down, but it slipped me mind."

Gran gave me a glance, over her spectacles. She knew I had acquired a trophy recently, could tell by the spring in my step, the sparkle in my eye.

"Well, well," she said, placidly, "I don't suppose it matters all that much."

"Oh, but it do." He squinted sideways through his goldfishbowl-glasses. "There's a gap in me fence, now, see. The dogs can get through." I had visions of all the local doggies queueing-up to get through the gap in his railings.

"They've killed off the boyslove bush I gave Annie years ago, and I'm afraid for me gladiolas. I tell 'ee, I'm worried sick about it. After all, you never know with dogs . . ."

After he'd gone, Gran said, "I'm afraid you'll have to take'n back."

It was no good saying I didn't know what she was talking about. Gran knew all.

"Why?"

"Because," she said, reasonably, "it ain't fair to rob the blind."

"He's not properly blind," I reasoned, but it was no use. Gran's judgements in moral matters were always conclusive. I waited until it was dark, and replaced my wonderful, shining golden spear.

Aunt Annie noticed it the next morning, and saw it as a Sign.

"Our railing's come back," she cried, "and guess what, Georgie, it's turned to gold."

He went out to see the wonder, remained doubtful of its miraculous transmutation, and scraped off the paint with his penknife.

"Is it a sign?" she asked.

He nodded.

"It is. Somebody's painted it."

"Do you think," she fluttered, "it came from on high?"

"No, love, I think it came from down low."

"We shall never know," she said, reverentially.

Uncle George chuckled, but didn't let on. He knew. He'd heard my Dad talking about gilding two picture-frames.

On the following Sunday he called in Gran's with a packet of tea, as usual, then said he'd like to see me, outside.

My heart sank. Retribution, I thought, is at hand. He led the way round the lilac-bush to the coal-house. Blinked, knowingly, through his magnifiers, and then, with a flourish remarkable in a man so nearly blind, produced my spear . . .

"Look what I've just found," he chuckled, "in the lilac bush."

I blushed with shame.

"Go on," he said, "take it. He's yours. I've replaced it with a strong bamboo. That'll keep 'em out, they dogs, and we couldn't have the one gold railing when t'others is black. It'd look queer."

"How about Aunt Annie?"

"Oh, don't worry about your Auntie, she'll think it's another sign. Shows we wasn't meant to keep the golden railing. It'll be a bit of a relief to her. She don't go in for show."

I promised I'd never tell her, and I didn't, but the funny thing was, the spear had lost its magic. I don't know how or why, but it wasn't the same. In the end, I swapped it with Shirty for a broken gramophone and one record which you could hear, faintly, if you turned it round by hand. The main-spring was broken, but it still had a voice-box, and Shirty showed me how you could change the voice from bass to treble by turning the record faster.

I got pretty tired of hearing that record.

> *Shepherd of the hills.*
> *I hear you cal-ling*
> *Shepherd of the hills,*
> *I'm coming ho-ome.*

And it's a funny thing, but although I heard it hundreds of times, and became heartily sick of it, that tune never failed to bring tears to my eyes. It still does.

———————

# Ackey Tarr

Ackey Tarr was the village character. More than a character. An original. A gargoyle. Under five feet tall, and thin, with a perpetual snigger and a wet nose like a dog.

If you saw Ackey without a dewdrop on his snitch, you knew he couldn't be well. There must have been excess water somewhere in his cranium, because his eyes watered, too.

He lived in a cottage over on the Common, with his donkey, Prince.

The donkey was his constant companion, when he wasn't grazing on the common – the donkey, I mean, Ackey ate civilized food, like jacket potatoes thrown in the embers and bacon cooked in an iron-age pan.

A proud little man, he never begged, hadn't claimed a penny from the Board of Guardians, and if he went hungry, he kept it to himself. How he came to be there, whether he was born or grew out of the Common, I never knew. He was like a survival from pre-history, a man without past or future, a gargoyle on the church tower, a crooked old tree. Children don't think that men like that were ever born, had parents, grew up.

Mind you, he had friends. Working, as he did, as an odd-job man, he was always in demand. Fetching and carrying. Moving things about. Doing a bit of hedging, repairing a gate, fetching in hay. Oh, no, he didn't lack friends. And he was quite normal in some ways. He drank beer, for instance, and played dominoes and went to chapel on Anniversary Sundays, and cultivated an allotment.

He'd never worn a collar or an overcoat in his life. He'd lost his teeth when I knew him, and that, with a tendency to splutter, made conversation with him difficult and – if you didn't watch out – wet.

His donkey was old, as donkeys go, and people said it would be a bad day for Ackey when the donkey snuffed it. You just couldn't imagine Ackey donkey-less. And 'Prince' couldn't last for ever.

But like Goldsmith's poem 'On the Death of a Mad Dog', it turned out otherwise. It was Ackey who fell ill. Caught a cold one Christmas, fetching in logs, and it went down on his chest.

"Have anybody seen Ackey lately?" they asked up at the Red Lion.

"Yes, I seed'n," says George Toop, "he's in a poor way. Took to his bed. Can't get downstairs."

"Who's looking after'n?"

"Missis-next-door takes 'n food and drink. Called the doctor. But there ain't much hope."

"Poor old Ackey. We better go and see'n."

So next day, three of 'em went down. Knocked. No answer. Went in, called out, no answer.

"We better go and ask missis-next-door."

"Go on upstairs," she said, "you'll be company for'n. He might have a last wish."

He did.

After they'd negotiated the stairs, which were crooked, like a dog's leg, they found him. In bed, all shrivelled up, croaking away like a raven, poor chap, in a bedroom so low they had to bend half-double to get in.

"How's it going', then, Ack?"

"We've brought 'ee a bottle of stout."

"You bin missed, Ackey, Red Lion don't seem the same."

He lay there, and wheezed, and tried to say something.

"Prop'n up with pillows," says George. "Give his voice a chance to get out."

They propped him up, gave him a swig of stout, and he found breath enough to ask:

"How's Prince?"

"He's out on the Common, Ackey. Don't worry about'n. He can take care of himself."

But Ackey persisted:

"I should like to see'n – just once – before I do go."

"You ain't going, Ackey."

"Cheer up, old chap. You got a lot of life in 'ee yet."

"Think about getting better."

Ackey shook his head. His eyes watered. Ominously, there was no dewdrop on the end of his nose.

"I should like to see'n once more, before I do go."

They looked at each other.

"Ackey," said George, "you shall. We'll bring en up here. It'll be hard work, up they stairs, but if that's what you wants, my son, that's what you shall have."

The others nodded.

"When?" croaked Ackey. "I mightn't be here long."

"Tomorrow," they said. "Just last out till tomorrow, and we'll bring en up."

Ackey closed his eyes and smiled. They left the rest of the stout, and crept out.

Next day was a Sunday, so they put on their bit-of-best and went down to the Common. Catching the donkey wasn't that easy, because he wasn't used to being caught by strangers, but they got'n at last and led'n to the cottage.

George went on in front to tell Ackey, he was coming, and the poor old chap came to himself for a while.

"I should like to see'n once more," he croaked. "We bin good friends."

They had a hell of a job getting that donkey up those stairs. I told you they were crooked, but I didn't mention they were steep and narrow and dark. It was murder to push him up. He didn' want to go. Well, when you come to think of it, it's not natural for a donkey to go upstairs.

If old Ackey hadn't raised his voice and called, "Prince! Princey! Come on then!" they'd never have done it.

But it was a case of His Master's Voice. He pricked up his ears, and went up they stairs like a long-dog.

They told me it was an affecting scene. Old Ackey, in bed, with his red nose sticking out of the blankets, and the old donkey licking him. Well, it must have been moving, because he up and died for joy of it. And they three chaps were left, at the end of the day, with a corpse and a donkey.

What was more, the donkey didn't want to leave. He'd found his master, and dead or alive, he didn't want to be parted. They had to call in missis-next-door to help, and of course she told 'em off for over-exciting the poor old chap.

I won't go into all the gruesome details of how they couldn't get his coffin down the stairs, and had to lower it out, on ropes, after taking out the window-frame. Nor how they got Prince out of the room by picking him up, bodily, and carrying him upside down. But it's a funeral that will always be remembered. The only one I ever heard of where one of the mourners was an ass.

Vicar wouldn't hear of it, at first, and then he changed his mind; "I've been thinking," he said. "It was on a donkey that Joseph and Mary took the infant Jesus into Egypt; and it was on a donkey that he entered Jerusalem, in triumph. The donkey can come ... But he'll have to stay at the back of the church."

There were people in the village – George Toop was one of them – who swore that the donkey wept. But I don't know. That seems a bit far-fetched. No doubt he missed the old fella. But he didn't pine away and die, as some said he would. He lived years.

The old chap hadn't left a will, and he didn't have any next of kin, so we boys claimed the donkey. We took him over, fed him, rode him, looked after him. He became a character, in his own right.

Ackey's Prince we used to call him.


'Course he's in heaven now. With all the other holy donkeys. And Ackey, of course. He'll be there. You can't tell me, characters like Ackey don't get to heaven. After all they must need a laugh now and then, even there.

Nicknames. Oh, yes, I completely forgot to tell you. How he came by his nickname. As I told you, he spluttered and he was toothless, and he was very polite. Whenever you gave him anything, he always said, "Thank you, ta!" Only it came out different!

"Ackey Tarr."

_____

# The Night the Bed Broke

It was the sight of that old brass bedstead, in a sale, the other day, that brought it back to me. Apparently, they're all the thing, now. Twenty–thirty years ago, they were thrown away or used to fill a gap in the hedge. Now they're collectors' pieces. . . .

My granfer and gran used to sleep in one, when I was a boy. I lived with them, and I remember it still. Wrought-iron curlicues, brass rails, and, above all, shining brass nobs. They unscrewed, you know. For a time, granfer, who was a miser, kept a little wash-leather bag with sovereigns in it, inside one of the bedposts. But gran discovered it, and he had to pretend he didn't know it was there.

"Must'a bin me father's," he said. He had to say that, because he'd been pleading poverty for years, saying he hadn't any money. It would have made him a liar if he'd admitted that he had this hoard all the time. So he said it must have been his father's, and that meant sharing it with gran, which he hated –granfer wasn't inclined to share anything with anybody.

In the cottage, they had the back-bedroom, I slept in the front, overlooking the lane. My room had a stuffed cuckoo, theirs a stuffed owl. Both rooms were a queer shape, with beams and angles, and theirs was at a lower level than mine. You went up the narrow, spiral stairs to my room, and then you had to go down two steps into theirs.

Most of their room was taken up with this bed. Apart from that, they had a marble-topped washstand, a gloomy picture of Mr Gladstone and Moses Surveying The Promised Land.

Did I ever tell you that both granfer and gran were on the big side? Well, to be honest, they were fat. He must have weighed eighteen stone, she seventeen. I remember once, at Weston, they both tried to discover their weight for one penny, and she stepped on as he stepped off, and the machine broke. Honest. It only weighed up to twenty stone, you see.

When the two of them got into bed at night, it would creak and groan, and the floor would groan, too, as though in sympathy. Well, I mean to say –thirty-five stone! They used to make beds in those days! I don't know how they managed to get into one bed – I used to lie awake, sometimes, and listen. I'd imagine what it must look like – that great pile of bedclothes, like a stranded whale!

As they settled down, there would be accusations from granfer that gran was taking up more than her space. She would say it was him, and the poor old bed would go *creak-creak groan-groan*.

Granfer usually seemed to get the worst of it.

"Oh, dear Lard!" he would complain. "Thees bin and kicked me in the stomach again. Why cassn't look what thees doin', 'ooman!"

"I can't help," she'd say. "I never did it a-purpose, Fred. I had this sudden spasm."

Granfer would tell the dear Lard that her spasms'd be the death of him yet.

Curled up in a ball, in my bed in the next room, I would wonder why people got married. Or, more especially, why fat people married other fat people!

It didn't seem right. After all, it wouldn't matter, if one of them was fat, the other thin. It didn't occur to me that when they were married they might not have been fat. At that age – I was eight – people – or rather, adults, seemed to be part of a timeless, ageless world. It seemed incredible that they could ever have been young or different. It was only my friends and my sister and I who changed, and then only very slowly, growing up.

In this early-morning age of timelessness and wonder, the night that it all happened, stands out in amazing clarity.

I was awakened by what I thought was an earthquake.

A tremendous crash, followed by cries for help and groans.

Taking up my tiny night-light, which I was allowed to have because I was sure that it was only the light that kept the demons at bay, I crept out of bed in my nightshirt to see what had happened.

The noise seemed to have come from the next bedroom. I lifted the latch, and opened the door, nearly tripped down the two steps, and then saw, by the wavering light, a scene of confusion . . .

At first, it was difficult to see what had happened. There were feathers in the air, and groans, and scattered bedclothes, which moved about like white-clad monsters. I put down the light on their wash-stand, and asked one of the heaving monsters:

"What's'matter, gran?"

"The roof have caved in," granfer's voice came back, muffled by sheets. "We'm shattered all to bits. I think me back's broke."

Gran was in the other pile. I could see her feet at one

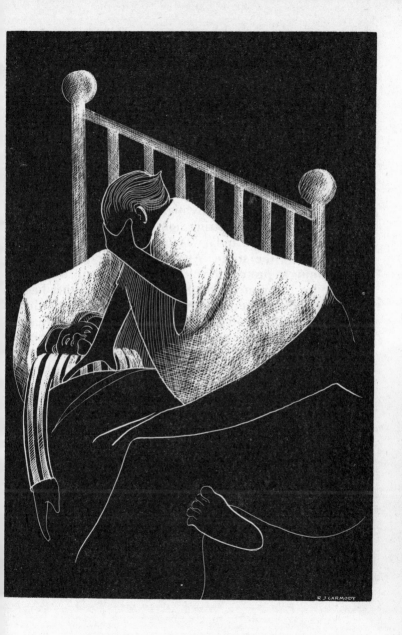

end, and I tried to help her disentangle herself. She was puffing and blowing with the effort, but she managed to say:

"See if you can light the big lamp, on the washstand, my son."

Normally I wasn't allowed to light lamps. Granfer considered it to be too dangerous to allow children to use matches. But this was different. This was an emergency. I found the lamp, took off the lampglass, and lit the wick from my nightlight.

It was an awe-inspiring sight. The bed was of solid iron, but jointed, and it was the joints that had broken . . . under the strain. After years of moaning and groaning in protest, the old bed had given up, at last – one leg had gone through the ceiling, the other had folded under, so that one end of the bed was on the floor, the other end up in the air. The bedclothes were in complete confusion, the bolster had broken open and leaked feathers everywhere, and granfer still lay there, under a pile of sheets, telling us that his back was broken, the house was down, and asking his dear Lard if it was the End of the World.

Together, we helped granfer escape. It was a strain, because he didn't help at all, just lay there and groaned that his back was broke. It wasn't. He moved fast enough when gran started poking about under the floorboards.

"Here, leave that alone," he said, "you'll have the whole house down."

"There's some sort of a sack or bag or something," she said, "under the boards".

"Thee cassn't do anythin' in the dark," he said. "We must get downstairs, whilst 'tis safe."

"I don't know how it came to happen," she said.

He said it was all her fault.

"You must'a turned over," he said, accusingly. " 'Tis the way you do do it – with a sort of a jump."

"Well, how else can 'ee turn over?"

"Like I do," said granfer, "slowly, with a roll, not a jump, like you do."

Next morning, he was up first, for the first time I could remember. Quietly removing a bag-full of coins from his latest hiding-place under the bedroom floorboards. When he had finished, and no trace was left, he woke up gran. By the time she came to look for the mysterious sack, there was nothing there.

As it happened, the bed wasn't a write-off. Walt, the blacksmith, mended it for them, and Uncle Philip patched up the floor. But there was no patching-up granfer. He now had a new complaint, to go with his asthma and rheumatism – a bad back! It came in handy whenever there was an awkward job to be done. He'd tell gran that he only wished he was up to that sort of job. Unfortunately, ever since that night when the bed broke because she'd turned over, he'd had this back.

It was a pity, she said, that blacksmith's couldn't mend bad backs as easy as they mended beds.

"Sometimes I wonder if your granny've got any feeling," he confided in me. "She never said she was sorry. She wouldn' admit, my son . . . women won't . . . that 'twas her fault".

As I say, I'd never have given that old bed a thought, but for seeing its identical twin at a sale the other week. Curlicues, brass knobs and all.

And d'you know that old bedstead fetched eighty pounds!

If only I'd kept the thing instead of stopping up a gap in the hedge, I'd be richer by eighty pounds, now — well, forty, anyway, my sister and I would share. But there you are, you never can tell what's going to be a collectors' piece and what'll be rubbish. Until it's too late.

———————

# The Blood Stream

Although I've told stories about Granfer Wilshire –
Chooky –my father's father, I don't think I've told you
about my Granfer Lewis.

They were as different as chalk and cheese.

Granfer Lewis, my mother's father, was tall and
rather thin, slightly stooping when I knew him, and
with a deep love of his cottage garden. He had a
moustache, black, with grey at the edges. Not a droopy
walrus moustache, nor a thin line of smacker, but a
decent, respectable, full-bodied growth of hair, out of
which his short black pipe protruded like a chimney.

My other grandfather was taciturn. Not so Granfer
Lewis. You might also call him loquacious on
occasion. Especially on the subject the first World War.

. . .

It was the only time he had ever left his native
village, and his reminiscences were full of references
to French villages, though they suffered such a
metamorphosis in his Anglicised pronunciations, that
I never had the slightest idea what or where they
were.

"We was bivvied in a wood," he would begin, "near
a little town with a queer sort o' name – Arkle or Arper,
it sounded like – and there was this chap in our lot who
played the Jew's Harp. Come from up North.
Birmin'ham, I think. We called'n Digger, a'cause he'd

bin a miner up North. Well, now, I happened to hear, years afterwards, that he got it in his leg one night, when he was on sentry-go. But that was years afterwards, years after what I'm saying about, now – the feller who told me about'n had been in the same hospital. But be that as it may," Granfer Lewis said, making a desperate clutch at the story-line, "we was bivvied in this wood, near Arkle (as near as I can get to't), when one o' the chaps (not Digger, this was a feller from Darset) said to me, he says, 'Bill' – that's what they called me, mostly, except for a cheeky little bloke from London, who called me Old Bill, which was coming it a bit, for this Old Bill was a carcature at the time – 'Bill', he says 'they woods is haunted . . .' "

By that time, however, Granfer would have lost his audience. He never seemed to realise that, if you set up as a storyteller, you've got to stick to the story. His family would be gossiping between themselves, telling how Mrs Rogers' leg was worse, and Fred Jackson was out of work again, how much potatoes were on the Hill, and there was a lot of it about at this time of year.

After a few minutes, Granfer would realise that he'd lost his grip, and that – me apart – his family were not with him in France. They had heard all his stories, long ago, and besides, there were so many interjections and wanderings that the point, when it emerged, seldom seemed to be worth the effort. He would put down his pipe on the hob of the fire, rest his head on the back of the chair, and fall asleep. His snores were as regular and as noisy as a steam-engine . . .

Now, I'm not being fair to Granfer Lewis. He *did* finish his stories, sometimes. It was only his war-

stories that never reached a conclusion. His personal anecdotes might be peculiar, but they were full of philosophy, and I couldn't understand why the family didn't appreciate their humour. There was that one about the blood stream. "The yewman body", he assured me, "is a marvellous thing. A world of its own. We got things in us, my son, that defy description. We got engines and pumps, 'lectricity and all. And we got our own rivers and lakes, valleys and mountains, pulleys and cranes and miles and miles of inner-tube".

"How d'you know?" I asked.

"I've seen it", he said. "You'd be su'prised how many bits you do see, after a bomb bursts".

For one awful moment, I thought he was going to get away to France, but he avoided the war, for once, took a pull at his pipe, to keep it alive, and went on. . . .

"I got this bit of a thorn in me finger, off the briars" – there were sweetbriar bushes all the way from the green gate down to the water-butt – "and although I searched for'n with a magnifying-glass and a needle, I couldn't find thik thorn. Me finger was main teart for a bit, but he never got septic. It'd got right through into me blood-stream, you see . . ."

He made me wait for the next instalment, whilst he puffed at his pipe. Then he said: "It must've been six months arter that that I was scratching me head, as you might if you had a sudden itch, like, when me finger pierced the skin and I felt something sharp in me head. Lord A'mighty, I thought, whatever's this, and I drew out" – he looked at me with intense seriousness – "The very same thorn", he said, "as went into me finger off our briar-bush."

Seeing my doubt, he said: " 'Tis like this, see –
that thorn had gone right through the skin, right
through into me blood-stream. We all got one. I
got one. You got one. We all got 'em – it do go
right round us, sometimes tricklin' a drop at
a time, sometimes rushin' along like a river in
flood.

"That tharn had bin washed along like a stick in a
brook – over waterfalls and through whirlypools – till
eventually he got to me head, on top of me scalp.

"Now, as everybody do know, the skin on top of our
heads is very, very thin – like paper. And when I
scratched, I broke through into the blood-stream jus'
as if I'd broke a bit o' thin ice."

My Gran, who had been listening, said wryly:

"Some might say the skin on top of your head is
more thin than most".

He didn't understand irony. Granfer said the skin
on his head was the same as the skin on her head. Men
and women, it made no difference to the skin on the
top of your head.

"Where's the thorn, now?" I asked.

He took his pipe out of his mouth, and pointed it at
his wife.

"I wanted to keep'n", he said, "as proof. But your
Granny wouldn' have it, not she. 'We don't want no
useless lumber', she cried, and out he had to go." "It
was just an ordinary thorn", she said, "nothing special
about'n at all."

"When I think of all the places that thorn had bin",
said Granfer, "right down to the tip of me toes, all
down through me innards, inside me heart and lungs,
and then to be thrown away as useless lumber".

"Tell me this, then", said Gran, "if you'm so clever –

how do this stream run uphill? I never heard of a real stream doing that".

"Ah, well", he said, profoundly, "that's where we differs from nature. That's the wonder on it. Some do say, 'tis the heart that pumps it round us, with never a stop, night or day. But however 'tis, I'm just saying the yewman body is a wonderful thing". And then he had to ruin it, by saying that that reminded him of an incident during the war. At a little place called – well, it sounded like Bovril, but it wasn't, these French people have got such a funny way of saying things . . .

He was off on another ramble in France, and just as the family had drifted off into a discussion of the price of vegetables and granfer would soon be drifting off to dreamland, I retired to the garden, his garden, with its rows of peas and beans and cabbages.

For a few minutes I speculated on the truth about blood-streams, and then I discovered that the goose-gogs were ripe and that seemed more important.

It was a summer's evening, and the air was full of the scent of honeysuckle and roses. Bees were working in the honeysuckle and the sweetbriar, and Granfer's gooseberries were distinctly more-ish. Briefly, I wondered whether they were starting on an odyssey, like Granfer's thorn, but at the age of ten you don't care all that much – I sent off a goodly number of goosegogs on a journey into the unknown.

---

# Off the Beaten Track

If you came to our house, you had to beware of two things – never stand near Dad when his fag-end exceeded an inch, and never, never get between him and the fire.

He suffered from catarrh, and when he spat, it was with unerring accuracy into the fire, where it would sizzle on the coals like a condemned soul in hell.

I don't know how many fags he smoked in a day, but I do know that his face looked incomplete without one. Usually with a long ash on the end, which you would watch, anxiously, waiting for it to fall.

Suddenly, he'd snort down his nose, and there'd be a snow-storm.

Dad was a docker. A casual worker on Avonmouth Docks, where he was well known for his small stature and large voice.

In those bad old days, dockers seeking work on a ship which had to be unloaded, stood in a "pen" to be selected, or "picked-up", as they called it.

Being a small man, surrounded by big chaps, Dad needed to attract attention. So he'd snort down his nose, have a spasm of coughing, start an argument – anything to remind the selector that he, Gilbert Wilshire, was there, and available for work.

When I was young, he used to embarrass my sister and I by speaking his mind in public. Especially on the subject of Bristol 'buses.

"Never bin the same", he'd say, "since Sir Stanley White's day".

Apparently the 'buses had never run to time since Sir Stanley withdrew his presence.

At week-ends Dad would forget the docks. We would escape into the countryside. Cotswold, Mendip, Severnside – we explored them all, on foot, with the assistance of Bristol 'buses.

He was the authority on 'bus time-tables, I considered myself the expert map-reader. So between us, we'd map out an interesting walk, and when, as often happened, we managed to get lost – the woods and fields resounded with Father's wrath.

Going home on the 'bus, he would inform everybody on the 'bus that this was the last time. "Never again!" he'd say. "I've had the lot! Been lost, chased by bulls, fell in a stream, and I'm wet through".

But when we reached home, it was another story. The exasperation had worn off.

"Had a good day?" Mother would ask.

"Never had a better", Father would assure her, cigarette adhering to nether lip.

"Right away from it all, Mother. Off the beaten track".

The funny thing was, he neither wanted a car himself or to obtain a lift in somebody else's. He looked on public transport as a social activity. An occasion to meet people, exchange views, argue with conductors and control the ventilation. He had this thing about windows . . . Either they were open too wide, creating a draught, or they weren't open enough and you couldn't breathe.

So his first preoccupation after finding a seat was to

sniff the air, critically, to ensure that it was fit to breathe.

Usually it wasn't. There would be "Excuse me's" and reluctant passengers expostulating, whilst Father opened a window here and closed another there. This would be on the top deck of a double-decker, of course. You weren't allowed to smoke downstairs.

Among conductors, he had few friends and one or two bitter enemies. Of these, Mary was outstanding. She was as fierce as Father and maintained that passengers should keep to their seats and only conductors allowed to control ventilation.

Cousin Daphne was on the top deck of a number

14, one day, when Mary came puffing up the stairs in a bad temper.

"What's matter, Mary?" enquired an unshaven gentleman with a red-spotted muffler. "Who upset thee now?"

"It's that Gilbert", she said. "I told him no seats upstairs and I wouldn't let him smoke standing on the platform. He's telling everybody what he thinks of me".

The red-spotted man and his companion laughed.

"Thee dusn't want to take no notice of he", said the muffler, "he's the same down the dock, ain't her, Fred?"

"When Gilb gets going", his companion agreed, "thee casn't stop 'n".

"He's only letting off steam", said No. 1. "Because he can't have a fag".

When she told Dad about it, he was indignant, wanted to know what they looked like, so that he could 'have it out with 'em'.

"Women conductresses', he snorted. "Should never 'a bin allowed. Poor old Sir Stanley must be turnin' in his grave."

With a flick of his tongue, he moved the stub of his fag to another corner of his mouth. "Unless, of course", he said reasonably, "he was cremated".

———————

# Telling Tales

A great teller of tales, my old man, especially to children.

I've known him stop kids crying, and end up with a bunch of 'em standing around, listening, fascinated, as though he was some sort of Pied Piper.

A favourite opening gambit was "How would you like a ride on my donkey?"

Or . . .

"Saw Father Christmas yesterday. He was asking me if I knew any boys who wanted an engine for Christmas".

In those days, children really believed in Father Christmas.

He was out-of-work at the time, so he hadn't anything else but stories to give them.

"When's your birthday?" he'd ask a little girl who was crying because she'd broken her doll. She'd stop crying and tell him, and he'd solemnly promise that she should have a new doll as a birthday present.

Of course, my sister and I knew they were only tales. We knew that, all the time he was handing out promises, the old man hadn't even the price of a packet of Woodbines – 2d for 5.

Mother would say, "Why do you promise kids things you know they won't get. Or if they do, it's no thanks to you?"

"I likes watching their faces," he said. "I like to see the light come back in their eyes".

"Hmph!" she said. "Think of the trouble their poor Mums and Dads have, making your tales come true".

He didn't tell *us* tales. Wouldn't have been much good. When the day came, and the present didn't arrive, we'd have made his life a misery. But the gipsy kids, over the Patch, believed every word. . . .

You'd see him, leaning against a wall, with a crowd of ragged, barefooted gipsy kids round him. "Next time I come this way", he'd be saying, "I'll bring my little donkey with me. Give 'ee a ride, if you want one".

Well, of course, they all wanted a ride on his donkey, and he'd solemnly take out a notebook and a stub of pencil and note down the names. Of course he didn't have a donkey. He didn't even like donkeys. But he could be very convincing, my old man. He could describe this donkey that he never had right down to the colour of its eye-lashes.

Next time he went that way, he'd have another story to account for the fact that there was no donkey with him.

"Poor ol' Ginger", he'd say, "he's too poorly to bring out. Off his grub. I'm having to keep him in the stable".

And finally, if the children persisted, Ginger would have to die. He'd describe that in detail, too. Have those tough little urchins crying, tears making white runnels down black faces.

"Never mind!" he'd say, "I shall be getting a new one. Got me eye on a nice little brown and white mare. If I gets her, I'll bring her down".

The effect on his audience may have been gratifying to him, it was embarrassing to us. We were always being pestered about the health of our non-existent donkeys, or asked if we'd ever been with him on the footplate of the Flying Scotsman. Father, according to them, was its driver.

We never actually told them it was a bunch of lies: that he was lucky to get two days' work a week on the banana boat. But he went too far when he told the gippos about Father Christmas. I suppose he'd lost his head a bit after his success with the donkeys. Anyway, it was very nearly the old man's undoing. They'd never heard about Father Christmas, or, if they had, thought it was nothing to do with them.

Dad made full use of their ignorance.

Told them how he (Father Christmas, that is) had a factory making toys for children, up at the North Pole. And on Christmas Eve he delivered them to all the children who hadn't been naughty.

"Shall we get any?" they asked.

"Depends on whether you bin good or not".

Well, of course, he was on safe ground there. They were a hardened bunch, and if receiving toys depended on being good it was obvious that Father Christmas wouldn't be coming their way.

One little boy said:

"What if we ain't bin good so far, but we'm good from now till Christmas?"

Father considered this with proper seriousness.

"Well, if you are – you'll get something. Mightn't be quite what you wants, but you'll get a present, provided, o' course, that you got a chimney".

He went on to explain that, unlike the postman, you didn't need an address for Father Christmas. He came

by air, and delivered by chimney.

Back in the shanty-town where they lived, no-one had ever told them such tales. They went home and demanded that they have a chimney. Didn't mind building it themselves. So long as they had a chimney.

One day, as Dad was walking up the lane, he was confronted by three truculent gipsy Fathers.

"We bin lookin' fer you", they said. One of them had a cosh. They looked ugly.

"Oh ah!" said the old man, taking a last long drag on his dog-end. "What about?"

"You bin tellin' our kids tales".

"No harm in stories".

"There is when we'm asked to build 'em bleedin' chimneys. We belts 'em round the earhole, but back they comes, 'We gotta have a chimney', they says, 'or he won't come'. We've told 'em straight that they won't be getting any toys. All they'll get is a leatherin', but they won't let it alone, and it's all your fault".

"Now, listen, you chaps", says Father, discarding his fag-end, "I got an idea, just you listen to me" . . . He was always at his best when he was in a tight spot. "Just you tell your wives" – that was a laugh, *wives* – "just you tell your wives to use the old toy routine. When they're paying their visits for old clothes". He was too tactful to say when they were out begging the Kind Ladies to give them their cast-off clothes. "At the same time as they're asking for clothes", says Father, "they can be asking for any old toys because their children haven't got none for Christmas. They'll find it'll work like a charm", he said.

And it did. They collected enough for their own kids and some left over to sell. And when the toys were found on Christmas morning, my old man's stock with the gipsy kids went up. They looked on him as a sort of prophet.

He should have gone easy after that, but he didn't. He told them stories like they'd never heard before. About a magical baby, born to a gipsy couple, in an old barn. How three caravans followed a star, and found the baby and worshipped him. His name was Jesus.

They'd never heard it, and were deeply impressed. Especially with the stories of miracles. My old man told them how this Jesus was persecuted, and starved in the wilderness, and promised the people who believed in him everlasting life. He told them that Jesus gave everything he had away, and told everyone else to do the same.

"That's one or two stories they won't forget in a hurry", he told us.

He was right. They took him at his word. Went back to the Camp, collected up all the things they'd pinched off other people, and gave them back.

As you can imagine, this was right against all their parents held dear. There was hell to play over there, across the Patch. Dad was warned that the men and womenfolk were out to get him, and if they did, they'd change the shape of his face.

"You've done it, now, Gilbert", Mum said.

"I'll keep out of their way", Dad muttered. "For the next few months I'll steer clear of the Patch. I'll use Tripe Alley instead".

It would be nice to say that they were converted, but the fact is, I don't know. They departed, soon after, during the night. Nobody knew where they'd gone, and we didn't particularly want to know.

———————

# When the Singing Stopped

My Father was contradictory about crowds. On Sundays, he liked to get away from it all, as he put it. Take a bus into the country, leave the city behind.

"If ther's one thing I like", he'd say, "it's the Open Road. Not to see another yewman bein' for miles".

Then, after a couple of miles without seeing anybody:

"Here, I hope you read that map right. We ain't seen a single soul to ask the way. I reckon we'm lost".

He may have liked the country, for a change, on Sundays, but he liked crowds, too. Saturdays, in Castle Street, with the hucksters and jostling crowds; at fairs and carnivals, with their cheap-jacks and steam-organs; and, above all, at Weston on the August Bank Holiday.

Not for anything would he miss Weston-Super-Mare on August Bank Holiday Monday. That was Life.

From our little railway-station at Staple Hill, they ran cheap day excursions. Half-a-crown. We saved up for weeks.

Back in those pre-war days, the station would be crowded. All our friends and neighbours would be there. People we'd been trying to avoid for ages. Father would put on his other self, shouting, "Hallo there, Jack, how be? How's the missis?" and "Come

45

on up this end, Mother – we're more likely to get a seat" and then "Ruddy engine's stopped short, get back, get back!"

My sister, Mother and I found it difficult to keep up with him, but he swept us along on the tide of his enthusiasm.

"Alice, come and look at this! . . . She must be twenty-five stone! I reckon if she gets in the sea, the water'll be over the prom. Now come on, you kids, help me with this deck-chair, the Collector's just gone past – we've got nearly an hour before he gets back . . . Mother, where's the sandwiches – no wonder they calls 'em sandwiches, they'm full of bleeding sand!"

We would push and shove onto the pier, queue for the toilets, and try to find a few square feet to paddle in the chocolate tide. Mother would have preferred to just sit and watch, but Father didn't want to miss a thing.

"Let's go up and see what's doing at the Old Pier", he'd say, or "Come on, it's better at Uphill".

"Just relax, Gilbert", Mother would say.

Not a hope. Father was afraid he might miss something.

Eventually, exhausted, we would make tracks for Locking Road. The crowds at the station were frightening.

"Leave it to me", said Dad. "Come on up here – no, back there – we'm on the wrong platform! Here's our train, coming in, now. Push towards the front, you kids. Quick!"

So convincing was he that there was soon a crowd of friends and neighbours following us. They themselves were confused, but Father had asked a porter. This

was our train. Now!

We would make a rush for the door, pile in, find seats, settle down, and Father was happy. Before the train had pulled out of the station he was leading the choruses of Tipperary, Bye-bye Blackbird and Happy Days Are Here Again.

One time, I remember, he was still leading the singing when the train went through Temple Meads.

"Dad", I tried to interrupt, "this isn't our line".

He was in the middle of Charmaine, and waved me away.

A few minutes later, I tried again, "Dad, we're stopping. It's a place called St. Anne's".

The singing stopped.

". . . St. Anne's? We'm on the wrong bloody train".

All Father's amiability vanished. He said things about that porter at Weston that I couldn't repeat. The people who had followed us, turned on him. The air was full of recriminations. On St. Anne's station, he told the porters and stationmaster what he thought about railways. It was a long walk home.

That, we thought, was the last time we would go to Weston on a Bank Holiday. But Father, with the resilience of the enthusiast, was never cast-down for long.

"Don't worry", he said, after the disappointment had worn off, "it'll never happen again. Next year we'll go by bus".

And we did.

---

# Force of Nature

My old man was very good at some things. But gardening wasn't one of them; he was no gardener. Nothing he planted ever prospered . . .

Mother's father, my granfer Lewis, was a first-rate gardener. He could grow *anything*; but my dad never possessed green fingers. He said it was a personal thing: a sort of war, which the forces of nature always won.

The forces of nature, he told me, were crawly things. Wood-lice and wireworms, leather-jackets, earwigs and caterpillars. Other people met with them, occasionally, but our garden was *full* of them. It wasn't earth – it was a solid mass of wireworms. When the old man planted potatoes, they never had a chance. The aggressive insects ate them as soon as they were planted. Cabbages never reached maturity: they were gobbled-up by caterpillars. *Thousands* of caterpillars! Carrots sometimes struggled up through the crust, but when they were exhumed, we only found a rotting corpse full of leather-jackets.

Mother said, "You might as well give it up as a bad job, Gilbert. They got it in for you, they crawly things. It's a waste of money to plant anything."

"I know," father groaned, "but it keeps 'em at bay. As long as I feeds 'em outside, they'll stay there, lyin' in wait. If they don't find food in the garden, Alice, they'll be in here after it. In the house."

He didn't care for nature in the raw, my old man, not if it included creepy-crawly things.

As my sister and I grew older, we took over the garden – as a tennis-court, cricket pitch and junk yard. Grass grew there, and that's about all. The skeletons of decaying bikes, scooters, prams and trolleys took over from the vegetables and father concentrated on what he was good at – clipping his hedge. He was a master at hedge-clipping. Not topiary, he never clipped them into shapes. Just square, like a wall – puffing a Woodbine as a protection against germs.

I suppose he thought the enemy below ground was content with grass-roots, until one day we heard a howl from the bedroom. It was father, and when he howled, you knew something was up!

He appeared, briefly, at the top of the stairs, dressed only in his long-johns and a vest.

"Quick!" he shouted. "Bring the Flit-gun. We'm invaded . . . Quick!"

We wondered what could be the matter, because it was not the season for wasps and mother was a vigorous housewife, always seeking out corners where things might lurk.

"What is it?" she asked. "If it's a spider in the bath run the 'hot' tap on 'im."

"It ain't spiders," he shouted, "we bin invaded by hard-backs. They'm all over the place. I warned 'ee, but you never took no notice."

We went up to see the invasion. My old man stood on the landing, shivering in his underwear, refusing to go into the bedroom.

"I opened a drawer to get me winter pants," he explained, "and it was full of 'em. Gert big 'uns."

"Where are they now?"

"Still there. I shut 'n quick, to keep 'em off me. Where's that Flit-gun?"

He directed operations from the rear.

"When I say 'Now' open the drawer, and when I say 'Shoot' give 'em full blast."

"I reckon you're making a fuss about nuthin'," mother said, but we children entered into the spirit of the thing. My sister waited for the order, and I held the Flit-gun.

"Now! . . . Shoot!"

I shot, and the room was full of Flit. When the mist cleared, we looked for bodies.

"Mind how you handle 'em," father said, when my sister pulled out his winter pants, "they might've survived."

They hadn't.

We found the remains of three small woodlice, that was all.

"Fuss about nothing," mother said, "you'm frightened of your own shadow, Gilbert – three little insects, and you rush around like a scalded cat."

The invading forces lay upside-down. One of them made a feeble motion with its leg.

"Flit!" father cried. "He ain't dead yet. He's strugglin' to get up."

"Poor things," mother commented, "just crept in somewhere warm, for the winter."

"Ah, my pants," father said, "just when I wants to creep into 'em meself. They don't look much, now, when they'm dead, but that Flit makes 'em shrink: they was twice that size when I seen 'em first."

And he wouldn't wear those pants until they'd been washed, twice, in carbolic. Even then, he had his doubts.

"They might'a laid eggs in 'em," he said, dubiously. "I shall never feel *at home* in these pants."

I only wish he was here, now, in these days of pesticides and sprays. He would have felt safe with a selection of them. They'll kill anything. You can get sprays for houseflies, ants, earwigs, caterpillars, greenfly, cockroaches, wasps – not that I believe in too much of this chemical warfare, mind – but it gives you a feeling of security.

I'll bet if he was alive, now, my old man would have the *lot*.

Or he would borrow mine. . . .

———————

# Father Christmas

One of my old man's favourite expressions was quids-in. If you were "quids-in", you were doing all right!

Another was "sup-me-bob" – this was an expletive, an expression of surprise. Must have been a contraction of "So help me, God!" but Father didn't know that, he used it, because on the docks, everybody used it.

He was peculiar, in some ways. He didn't like Christmas. I don't suppose it *is* much fun, if you're short of money, and it's a bad time of year down at the docks, with not many ships coming in. If you didn't work, you weren't paid, in those days.

Anyway, he always ridiculed the old gentleman in the red cloak, and the giving and receiving of presents which cost you dear and weren't what you wanted.

"Terrible waste o' money," he grumbled. "They've only got to hear a few carols and see some holly and mistletoe, and they goes mad."

We solved the problem of Christmas presents eventually, by an "arrangement". He gave me something *he* wanted, and I gave him something *I* wanted. Then on Christmas morning we solemnly returned our presents. It worked out quite well!

I remember one year I gave him a map of the Mendips, and he gave me a magnifying glass. That must have been in later life, when he couldn't see to read the Obituaries in the evening paper.

But that was after I was grown-up. When I was a kid, Mother bought the presents. She loved Christmas. All the shops lit up, the decorations, Christmas trees, holly – Mother would get all excited, and boil the Christmas puddings in basins, ten or twelve of them; enough, Father said, to bung up our insides for the rest of the year.

As I say, Mother bought the presents. One year, I remember, she bought me a mouth-organ. It drove the old man mad. He told her she should have had more sense.

"Givin' a thing like that to a boy who can't play'n," he said, "it's like givin' a hand-grenade to a hottentot. Me head's fair splitting!"

"It's Christmas, Gilbert!"

"Christmas!" he said, disgustedly. "'Tis more like bleedin' bedlam!"

"The boy's got to practice."

"*Practice*? If he'd'a practice ten years, he on't master that thing. All he da do is *blow, suck, suck, blow* – it may be practice to somebody tone-deaf, but I got an ear for music, and I tell 'ee straight, it's drivin' me up the wall."

In the end, he couldn't stand it any longer, and he gave me six-pence to go and play outside.

"Go and annoy the neighbours," he said, "I can't stick it no longer. It's like twenty cats bein' sick. Sup-me-bob, I wonder sometimes whether your Mother wants to be rid of me. She knows I got sensitive ears."

So I went round the neighbours, with my mouth-organ, playing carols, and it was quite surprising how generous they were. Perhaps they had sensitive ears, too!

Shortly after Christmas, however, the mouth-organ vanished, and though I searched high and low, it was not to be found. I reckon it's probably lying in the mud at the bottom of Avonmouth dock.

My sister had a pram that year. She had no dolly to put in it. Mum and Dad couldn't run to both, so she made-do with a stocking, filled with paper. Father drew a face in indelible-pencil on the top and tied it into shape with string. The arms and legs weren't too good, and the final result was what you might call grotesque.

She said she couldn't *cuddle* it.

"Pretend," Mother said, but she said there was a limit to pretending.

Anyway, she only had to wait twelve months, till the next Christmas, for a real doll. I remember it. China, it was, with a simpering face and eyes that opened and closed. If you pressed the squeaker in the small of its back, it was supposed to say *mama*. Only they must pronounce it differently in Japan, or else it didn't work properly. What came out was a sort of broken squawk. This was another thing that got on Father's nerves. He said it was more like the death-agonies of a rooster than a baby saying Mama.

However, she dressed it up, put it in the pram, and took it out to show off to her friends in the street. Almost immediately, there was an agonised cry and a crash.

She had tipped up the pram, negotiating the kerb, and her new doll was lying in the gutter. We rushed out to see what had happened, and at the awful sight Father let loose a few ripe expressions that were

usually reserved for careless crane-drivers.

The doll, the china-doll, that had cost one-and-eleven pence in Bristol, was in a hundred fragments. The eyes had fallen out and rolled away. The squeaker that said *Mama* was waterlogged in a puddle. We picked up the pieces, but my sister refused to touch them. She wanted her dolly, she sobbed, and Mother said, "And so you shall, dear. Your Father's a dab hand with the egg-white. Don't you worry. He'll soon have it fixed. You won't know the difference."

"Whassmean?" Father demanded. "I can't mend that. He's bust to smithereens. Look facts in the face, Alice – that doll's had it!"

My sister burst into tears. Mother told him not to be unreasonable. After all, it was Christmas. She'd waited all the year for that doll, and then – a slip – and there it was, broken.

"You ought to have known, when you bought'n," Father said, wearily. "Cassn't get 'em made of rubber? You know she's rough with things."

He grumbled, but in the end he got to work with the egg-white, and worked on that doll all day. It ruined our Christmas dinner, seeing him there, wild-eyed and unshaven, with a strong smell of egg-white around him.

Eventually, quite late in the evening, it was finished. "What's think of that, then?" he asked, proudly handing the china-doll to my sister.

She took one look at it, and burst into tears.

"What's the matter with 'er, now?" he demanded.

"The eyes don't look quite right," Mother hazarded. "She looks sort of . . . squint-eyed."

"Well, I can't help. P'raps the wire got a bit bent. It's

all very well for they Japs, they got small hands, but it's a hell of job, to get 'em right. As 'tis, they on't shut. I had to glue 'em in, see."

"Pity," Mother said. "Try the *Mama*-thing, dear."

She did, and a sort of strangled gasp came from the doll.

"It works," Father said, but once again my sister had started to cry.

"What is it now?" he asked.

"She . . . she looks old," my sister said, "all those cracks."

"Well, o' *course* there's cracks, that's where I had to stick her together."

I could see what my sister meant by looking old. What with all the cracks, the doll didn't look like a baby. More like a squinting dwarf. Sinister at that! – When you come to think of it, it's surprising she turned out to be such a good mother – my sister, I mean. She swapped the doll for some marbles. The boy opposite thought the doll looked a bit like his school-teacher, and he wanted it for "experiments". I had a suspicion that the "experiments" entailed sticking pins into the doll, and hoping to evoke the powers of darkness. Anyway, it all turned out all right in the end. My sister turned out to be a dab-hand at marbles. All for the best, when you come to think of it!

———————

# Jacko

It isn't his right name, and his name isn't Jack, either. But somehow it fitted him. He had a sort of wise-monkey look about him, when he was a kid. He grew out of it, and of course he's not Jacko now. He's a respectable businessman, well-known in a certain village near Bristol, a pillar of the local community. I'm probably the only man who remembers him as Jacko.

When we were at school, junior school, he was a tartar. We had a headmistress, Miss Fogg – we called her Foggy – who was short, fat and pompous. She had a moustache.

Some of the kids said that if she didn't shave, she'd have a beard too. Be that as it may, she certainly had a moustache. Black it was, like her eyes.

Every day, when it was Time, at the end of Play, and after lunch, she'd puff and blow her way into the middle of the playground and solemnly ring her bell, her big brass hand-bell, exactly ten times. At the end of it, she would expect all playing and talking to have stopped. Silence. Dead silence. Whatever you were doing, you had to stop, and then, after half a minute, she'd ring her bell again, and we had to fall-in, two-by-two.

It was a tense and solemn moment. Like armistice. And you can imagine the effect when, after she'd rung her bell for silence, a solitary voice shouted "OIL!"

We couldn't help laughing.

Because Jacko was a mimic, and he was imitating Billy Butterworth, our local oil-man, who also rang a bell when he went on his rounds with his iron-wheeled cart. "OYULL," he used to call. He sold paraffin. We used a lot, in those days, for the lamps.

Of course, Foggy wouldn't know Billy, because she lived in Clifton. And she didn't see the joke. She caned him, and kept us in half-an-hour for "encouraging" him.

We called him "Oyull" for a few months, after that – but we went back to Jacko, in the long run – it seemed more suitable.

When we were in our 'teens, at what we called Big School, Jacko did not distinguish himself much at lessons, but gained a great reputation among the boys as a parodist.

We had a music-teacher, a very serious-minded man who taught us folk-songs and carols. Old Jonesy. "Cherry Ripe" and "When I went down to Strawberry Fair". But Jacko composed parodies, which caught on like wildfire. We sang –

*When I went up to Rodway Fair*
and
*Hairy tripe, hairy tripe, tripe I – I cry-y,*
*Bull and bare ones, co – o – me and die*

Not *really* very funny; but we all sang it with enjoyment, until old Jonesy found out, and he regarded it as heresy. He found out who was behind it when we were singing that well-known carol –

*While shepherds wash their socks by night*

And Jacko had to write out "I must not try to be funny," a hundred times.

The trouble was, Jacko couldn't help expressing his humour. Every white post around the village he lived in bore examples of his wit – verses, usually rude.

It wouldn't have received official attention, if our teacher, Dobbin, hadn't taken his family out into the country for a week-end walk. He chose the country in which Jacko lived, so every white post and stile they passed displayed verses, one or two of which were directed at Dobbin.

Dobbin knew who was author of them by the writing. Exposed him, in Hall, the Monday following. "Miserable boy," he called him, between whacks of the cane. He hadn't been miserable before, but Jacko was certainly miserable afterwards.

It was good advertising, though: nearly every boy in the school made the pilgrimage to Jacko's village. Just to see what had ruined Dobbin's day in the country.

. . .

Those who left it a bit late missed seeing anything, though, because Dobbin wrote to Jacko's parents, and they made him go all the way round the village, scrubbing out his verses.

Jacko gave up writing poetry, after that. In fact, he had started going to the pictures and discovered that he bore an uncanny resemblance to James Cagney. He did have a sort of Cagney look about him, bright and cocky, full of cheek. And he had a talent for chatting-up birds. We called him "Cag", and envied him his self-assurance. Until he fell victim to his own success, and had to marry the girl.

After that, he went out of circulation and I never saw him until recently. But that's the advantage of living in

the same place all your life. You don't lose touch. Anecdotes have a way of becoming stories, given time.

Nearly a lifetime later, I met him again. Outside his shop. Of course he's a very different person, now. Respectable. Pillar of society. Nice detached house, member of a golf club, puts up for the council.

I'm not going to tell you what sort of business it is, because that'd be giving the game away, but I can tell you that Jacko is a success.

He'd just had his premises painted, brilliant white, and he was standing outside, looking at it.

He didn't recognise me at first.

"Look at that!" he said. "Vandalism. Ought to be stopped."

On the blank white wall at the side of his shop, somebody with a spray gun had written in giant letters "CITY RULES O.K."

I said it was terrible, and it was. But I couldn't help remembering Jacko and his rude verses on gateposts. They didn't have spray-guns, in those days, but if they had, Jacko would have been one of the first of us to get one.

"It wasn't done by a kid," he said, "I can tell you that for starters."

"How d'you know?"

He looked slyly at me – almost like the old Jacko – "Those letters," he said, "begins six feet from the ground. A kid couldn't reach that far."

"Who do you reckon, then?"

He became solemn, almost pompous. "One of my political opponents," he said. "They thought they'd score off me. It's known hereabouts that I'm a strong city-supporter."

I must have looked dubious at this, because he added portentously, "those words went up the very week – the very week – City went down the pan. As soon as they knew we'd be relegated."

"Didn't you tell the police?" I asked.

He exploded.

"Don't talk to me about the police. I said to 'em, I said, 'Where's your handwriting expert? I want the culprit traced.' But I might as well have been talking to a brick wall; they thought it must be boys. 'That's not the work of boys,' I told 'em. 'I can give you six names. Six. Check up on their handwriting, and you've got your man.' "

"What did they say to that?"

"Said I was over-reacting. Me! Over-reacting! The trouble is, the authorities are too soft, these days. There's vandalism everywhere. Time they brought back the birch!"

I was thinking of our schooldays – of the time he'd shouted "OIL" and parodied serious songs. And because I was far away, I let it slip out . . .

"You're right, there, Jacko!" I said, without thinking. It was a slip of the tongue, that "Jacko", but it went home.

He stared at me as if he'd been stung, realised who I was and what I remembered, and without another word, turned and went into his shop.

I don't suppose he'll ever speak to me again, but if he's reading this – which isn't very likely, because he's a busy man, these days – I want to tell him that it wasn't I who sprayed "CITY RULES O.K." on the wall of his shop.

I mean to say, do I seem like the sort of man to spray words on walls! And anyway, I'm a City supporter, myself.

---

# The Year of the Trolley

I suppose grown-ups would have known it as the Year of Amy Johnson, or Mae West, or the Loch Ness Monster or the R.101. It was the early 1930s – dole-queues and Hollywood musicals.

To me, it was the Year of the Trolley.

Every red-blooded boy of my age had one. There were even two-trolley families. And the actual vehicles themselves varied – from the basic model of a plank and four pram-wheels, to *de luxe* versions with a brightly-coloured biscuit-tin as chassis and a tea-box for cab.

Mind, I was lucky. My old man wasn't a Do It Yourself fanatic, more of a Leave It To Somebody Else man. That left him free to exercise his talent on imaginative projects. He was an expert kite-maker, very good at hutches and swings and he excelled himself in the matter of The Trolley.

Apart from his talent, my old man had some natural advantages. He was always young at heart, mother called it childishness; he'd been brought up to shoemaking, so he knew what to do with a hammer and nails; and since they were reduced to two days work a week on the docks, he had plenty of time to concentrate on the important business of trolley-making without the distraction of a regular, Monday to Friday job.

What he created was a masterpiece: a trolley which

made the other kids in our road green with envy. It was a double-plank job, w·h two small wheels on a bogy at the front, so that it could be steered, and two big wheels at the back. A soap-box provided the cab, the hood of an old pram turned it into a convertible, and the motive power, as always, was by foot. You just sat on the back of the cab, and pushed with your feet. We called it scuffing.

Of course, the scuffer was inferior to the driver, who sat in the cab and steered. It was a two-man operation. The scuffer could only see what we'd passed, the driver had to concentrate on what was ahead. The driver was in charge, and he told the scuffer to push harder when you went uphill and to stop scuffing when you went down.

It was pretty heavy on the footwear, mind. Boots (nobody in our *milieu* wore shoes) wore out in no time, what with scuffing and braking. The scuffer used his boots for braking, going downhill, applying pressure gently to the rims. It had to be gently, because if you braked hard it upset the trolley and broke your leg.

There was a gulf between scuffers and drivers. You were only a driver if you owned a trolley, and then you had to choose your scuffers with care. Some were unreliable, likely to desert when the hills got steep. A really good scuffer was worth his weight in toffees. You had to give him a "go" at driving, sometimes, to keep him sweet, and for long journeys you paid him in the currency of that time – cigarette cards.

Wouldn't work now, of course. Streets were playgrounds, then. Motor traffic hadn't yet taken over. Horses and carts were natural hazards, but the greatest danger came from girls' skipping-ropes. Honestly, they thought they *owned* the street! Tied their rope to a lamp-post one side, and one of 'em, whose turn it was, turned the rope on the opposite pavement. As she turned, they chanted –

> *My mother says,*
> *I never should*
> *Play with the gypsies*
> *in the wood!*

We used to have lots of these rhymes in those days. Counting-out rhymes and jingles like *Penno'th o' chips, to grease your lips, and out goes he* (or *she*, as the case might be). . . .

Anyway, looking back, I'm amazed how far we used to go on those trolleys. Fishponds. Staple Hill park. Roddy Hill. All over the shop! Of course, there were accidents – well, you had to expect it – but I can only remember one disaster.

That was the day we went to Moorend.

We should never have gone, in the first place. Moorend was out of bounds. A relation of mine had been drowned there, in the river – and mother never let me forget it.

For that reason, it was the one place I wanted to go. The only trouble was that for a great expedition like that you needed not just a scuffer but a crew. Good chaps, with strong legs and solid boots. Chaps who wouldn't talk about it afterwards.

So three of us – Don, Dennis and I – set out, one Saturday, on the fateful mission. We agreed to take the scuffing in turns, but it was a hot day, and by the time we got there, we had sore feet. The river Frome runs alongside the road there, and it looked very cool and inviting. We took off socks and shoes and went for a paddle.

There were all sorts of interesting things to do. Discovering islands, and an old mill, catching tiddlers in our hands and letting them swim away again, building a dam . . . We were lost to the world, as they say, when Don said suddenly:

"Where's the trolley?"

We looked around us, in dismay. We'd wandered far away from the place where we'd left it, on a high bank, by a sycamore tree.

Retracing our steps along the river, we found the steep bank and the sycamore tree, but not the trolley.

"Somebody's pinched it!" Dennis said.

Don, who was older and therefore wiser, said:

"P'raps it ran down the bank, into the river."

"How could it?" I asked. "Couldn' run away, on its own."

"We never tied it up. Didn' even put a stone under the wheel."

Straightaway conjecturing that it might have floated downstream, we set off in our bare feet, to follow the stream, through a thicket, across some fields, and there – caught up against a weir – was our trolley, upside-down, with its wheels in the air.

The canopy, never all that secure, was missing; but apart from that, it seemed more or less intact. We got it out and on the road, and were ready to start back home, when we realised that something was missing. Our socks and shoes. They'd been in the cab of the trolley, and must have tipped off into the river.

It was too dark to look for them, by that time, so we scuffed home with bare feet. And if you've never scuffed a trolley home in the dark, up hill and down, for three or four miles, with rain running down your back, and no shoes on, you don't know the meaning of the word 'misery'.

I was in bed with a cold and bronchitis after that, so I escaped inquisition. Don and Dennis weren't so lucky. They spun their mother a tale of being set upon by a gang of roughs from the New Buildings, who stole their shoes and socks – they couldn't tell the truth, because, as I said, Moorend was out-of-bounds. Nobody believed them, of course. They had their pocket money docked for a month, but I was lucky because, as I was at Death's door, I was cossetted, and it wasn't until afterwards, when my dad saw the state of the trolley, that I was in danger of being blamed.

"Here, you bin and lost the canopy," he said. "One or two of the spokes is bent. What bin happening?"

"It was an accident," I said. "He ran away."

"Some boys would'a had more respec'," he said bitterly. "I know boys who'd'a given their eye-teeth for a trolley like she."

I knew that was true, but wanted to avoid further explanations. I've never been much good at lying. So I resorted to a trick I've used once or twice since. I changed the subject.

"Sidney Olive said he'd give me a rabbit for my old kite", I said.

"Did er say what sort?"

Father had a soft spot for rabbits, provided they weren't Belgian Hares.

"Never mind what *sort*," mother said. "What sex is it? That's what matters, with rabbits. We don't want thousands of little rabbits round our back."

"It's a buck," I said, happily, "White Angora".

It worked. Father's imagination went to work at once. He said he could make a very tidy little hutch out of Aunt Lily's old chest-of-drawers which was residing in our coal-house.

I took down my old kite from the top of the wardrobe, and brought home the white Angora. In a shoe-box, with holes in it for the rabbit to breathe, on the back of me trolley.

———————

# The Lump

Looking back, you realise that certain moments – minutes, hours, days, happenings – changed you. Not so much in later life, you tend to be less affected by happenings, as you get older.

When you're young, though, a break in the routine really hits you. I remember my Illness, across fifty-odd years, with extraordinary clarity – which is strange, considering that I'd forgotten about it, by the time I was ten.

It's true, as you get older, you remember more – about your childhood. Not the ordinary things of life, but your first taste of fear, joy, love, horror, self-awareness.

I had this lump-thing on my neck. It grew and grew, till it pushed my head sideways, and people remarked on it.

"I'd take'n to see the doctor, if I was you," they told my mother. "He's goin' lop-sided."

"It's a boil," mother said.

They looked at me, and shook their heads.

"Too big for a boil," they said.

Uncle Sid, always facetious, said, "May be growing another head."

"How horrible," Auntie May shuddered.

"Make 'is fortune," her husband assured her: "Lewis – the two headed man."

After they'd gone, mother wept quietly into the aspidistra.

"We shall have to go," she said. I knew where. Dr. Mac.

His surgery was at Kingswood, where the shopping-centre is, now – gas-jets and people coughing. Medicines dispensed on the spot.

Although I was fearful, seeing my mother's tears and knowing nothing about doctors, Dr. Mac proved to be a very comfortable sort of man. He sat me on his knee, showed me his watch, and examined the lump on my neck.

"Will you have to lance it, doctor?" mother asked.

He shook his head.

"No, I don't think so. Don't get alarmed, but I think he should see a specialist."

At the word "specialist", mother wept. Dr. Mac soothed her, gave her a note, and we came away.

"I won't have to go away, will I?"

At the age of six, this seemed the ultimate in horror.

"No, no. I won't let 'em," she blubbered; which, of course, made me more fearful than ever.

"What did er say?" father asked when he came home from the docks.

"Gave me a note," mother trembled. "For a – *specialist*."

"Now, then, Alice, no need to get upset. It mightn't be anything much. You'll upset the boy. You know how he takes things to heart."

For a few days, there was silence. I asked when I'd have to see the specialist, but mother put on her artificial laugh and said I mustn't fret myself, the lump

was going down, I should be "all right". And then, one
sunny June morning, she said we were going into
town.

Was it the specialist? I asked.

No, no – we're going to the zoo.

Was she sure? It wasn't – couldn't be – the
Hospital?

Oh, no – whyever did I imagine a thing like that?
Hospital? She hoped I'd have no call to go *there*.

We went in on the tram, and she carried a suitcase.
It was a few things she had to deliver, she said. I would
like the zoo – all those animals – lions, tigers, sealions,
camels.

Why do we have to walk up this hill? I wanted to
know. Is this the way to the zoo?

Mother kept blowing her nose. She said she had a
cold coming. And when we turned into this big
building, she said it was to deliver the case.

It wasn't until we were in a room with a nurse, that I
realised this *was* the hospital. The nurse told my
mother, she could leave the case behind, and needn't
worry. She turned away, and I said, "Mum – don't go!"
She came to me, crying, and held me tight. "I won't,"
she said, "I won't go." But after a minute or two, the
nurse said, "Come along, Mrs. Wilshire – we've got to
get him into bed."

Weeping, mother left and the nurse said briskly,
"Come along, son – get your clothes off. Put these
on."

She handed me a pair of brown pyjamas. Not mine.
Hospital pyjamas.

"I want to go home."

"Now, don't be silly. Be a brave boy. Show me how
quickly you can undress."

I'd never undressed in front of a stranger and I was determined not to, now. The nurse started to unbutton my coat. I fought to keep it on. She called for help, and I was undressed.

Humiliated, abandoned, I was forced to wear the hated brown pyjamas.

"He'll be better when he gets in the ward," an older nurse said, "when he meets the others."

I didn't want to meet the others, or go in the ward – I just cried and cried – all their pleas to be a big boy only made matters worse. It upset the other children so much that they took me out into the garden, tried to amuse me, when all I wanted was to go home.

I cried so much that day that I've never been able to do much crying since. Reckon I must've exhausted the tear-ducts or something.

They operated next day, removed the lump and my tonsils, as well, and I overheard them telling my mother that the operation was a complete success.

"It was touch and go, at one time," said the specialist. "We'd finished the operation, and his tonsils were inflamed, so we had to operate again, and take them out, too."

Of course, mother fussed over me, and so did everybody else. I was suddenly a hero.

But I was never the same again. It made me wary. The operation itself was nothing, and hospital wasn't so bad, either, it was being decoyed there, and left – abandoned, in a pair of strange pyjamas.

The worst thing I can imagine, still, is being in a strange bed, in a pair of strange pyjamas.

You aren't yourself, any more, you're a patient. And they smell – or those did – the worst sort of smell – disinfectant.

Mind you, I've been in hospital and had operations, since, but they were casual affairs, not worth remembering. In fact, I went of my accord, and quite enjoyed the rest.

No, it was the sense of desertion, that time. A sort of betrayal. I know it's not logical: I had to go and mother had to leave me. It was getting undressed and having to put on brown pyjamas that did it. And the smell of that disinfectant. . . .

———————

# Big School

"When you come back from holiday," she said, "you won't be coming back here. You'll be going to Big School."

There was a stunned silence.

"Why can't we stay here, miss?" Edith Larkins asked.

"We don't want to go to Big School," several others chorused.

With assumed brightness, Mrs. Iles said: "Time to move on. You're big children, now."

We didn't *want* to be big children! From what we'd seen of Big School, the Infants was better: cosier, happier, more comfortable.

Amy, who was a terrible cry-baby and who always hid under her desk when there was thunder about began to cry. Edith joined her, along with several other girls. I felt the tears pricking my eyelids, but being a boy, I wouldn't let them through.

"You'll like it when you get used to it," Mrs. Iles said, consolingly, but her voice broke slightly and we could tell she wasn't far off tears herself.

"Please, miss," one of the boys said – I think it was Walt Lukins – "whose class'll we be in?"

"Miss Daker's."

Even the girls stopped crying, paralysed with fear.

Big School was bad enough, after the easy-going

79

Infants, but Miss Daker was a name which struck terror into the hardiest of us. We had seen how rigid the rules were in Big School, we had heard, across the playground, the savage instructions to stand still, sit up straight, answer the question, tell the truth. That was bad enough. But Miss Daker was a name only whispered in corners, an embodiment of anger, accusation and enmity – from whom no weakness could be concealed, all-seeing, all-hearing, taut as a spring.

Mrs. Iles said goodbye, and touched us, each in turn, kissed Amy and gave Edith Larkins a hug, and we left childhood behind for ever.

Usually, we raced home, happy as colts in a field. Today, we stood about, numbed with foreboding, whispering about the wrath-to-come, telling each other tales we'd heard about Miss Daker, already standing in corners, isolated, ridiculed, snapped at, humiliated.

On our first day in Big School, we were initiated into Assembly. Everybody stood up, in the room they called Hall, and the headmaster, Mr. Pearn, waited for silence.

We had never had silence before. It seemed unnatural. Mr. Pearn was middle-aged and autocratic. He represented Authority.

"I shall not begin," he said, "until I have silence."

We held our breath, afraid to move. After an eternity, he said: "Today we have new boys and girls among us. They will see what is expected of them, and behave. Let us pray."

In sing-song, the entire school recited the Lord's Prayer. We didn't know what it meant, and it was some time before I got it sorted out. "Our Father, which art in heaven," (but mine worked on Avonmouth docks), "Harold be his name," (my old man's name was Gilbert), "give us this day our daily bread," (ours was delivered by George Phillips' roundsman, and I knew it wasn't free, because I'd heard Gran confide in one of her cronies, that she was behind with the bread-money), "forgive us our trespasses, as we forgive them that trespass against us," (that must be something to do with the fields, down by Snuffy's, which had notices TRESPASSERS WILL BE PROSECUTED), "deliver us from Eva," (she was in our class, and I made a mental-note to steer clear of her, in future), "for Thine is the Kingdom, the Power and the Glory, Forever-andever, *Ahmen*!"

At this point, Amy started to cry, and was removed. The rest of us shuffled our feet and opened and closed our mouths, as if we were singing the hymn.

Then we were ushered into a room, with hard desks and high windows and Miss Daker.

She, too, wanted silence.

Complete silence, before she began, telling us, sharply and decisively, that it was about time we woke up, learned how to behave, had *discipline*.

"Please, miss, can I leave the room," said Jabby Little – we called him jabby, because he kept jabbing you with his forefinger.

"Certainly not!"

Our hearts sank. This was it. Discipline. You couldn't even leave the room!

"I want to see what you can do," Miss Daker said. "Write this down as I dictate. In ink. You don't use pencils now."

We picked up pens and tentatively dipped them

into inkwells. Some children tried to use them with the nibs upside-down, others made blots, I felt secure in the knowledge that I could write with pen-and-ink. In Mrs. Iles' class, I'd been top of the class at writing.

"Once upon a time, there were three brothers" . . . several of the girls started to cry . . . "the oldest was called Gilbert, the second one James and the youngest George."

It was obvious that the new class were not up to this standard. Miss Daker looked around angrily.

"You," she said, "what's your name?"

"Jack."

"Don't speak to me like that. Before you answer, always say, 'Please, miss. Now . . .'"

"Please, miss. Jack, miss."

"I'm not interested in your *first* name. What's your other name?"

"Please, miss: Jones, miss."

"That's better. Show the class what you've done, Jones. Hold it up."

He held aloft a sheet of paper. It had several blots and very few words on it. Miss Daker's glance was scathing.

"You disgust me, Jones. Come out here."

He went out to the front, taking his dictation with him.

"Stand in the corner," she said, "facing the wall. We don't want to see you, Jones."

She looked around the class, thought she detected a certain smugness, and next thing I knew, she was pointing at me.

"You," she said. "Stand up. What's *your* name?"

"Please, miss, Wilshire, miss," I mumbled.

"Speak up; I can't hear."

My face was crimson with shame and embarrassment.

"Show the class *your* efforts, Williams."

They knew my name was Wilshire, and I didn't dare contradict her. I held up the page, expecting approval.

"What's this?" she exclaimed sharply, deciding that it was necessary to make an example of someone, "baby-writing? Is *this* all you've learned? The letters are not joined-up!"

"No, miss, please, miss, we wasn't . . ."

I was going to explain that we'd never been taught to join up letters, but Miss Daker had chosen me to be first victim.

"I will *not* have baby-writing. We write properly, here, like this . . ."

She wrote the paragraph she had quoted on the blackboard, in stylish copper-plate, and we copied it, or tried to. Once again, she chose me to be scapegoat. Not, I think, because my attempt was worst, but because she'd decided that, if she chose mine as a bad example, those who knew their attempts were worse, would set their standards high.

In the past, I'd never experienced this sort of thing. It worried me, because no matter how hard I tried, my attempts aroused scorn.

And that wasn't all. My bowels began to play up.

"What is it, this time?" Miss Daker would say.

"Please, miss, may I leave the room?"

"No."

"Please, miss, I've got to."

Our toilets were primitive, even for those days. Across the playground. Miss Daker watched through the window, to see that you actually went; and if you were a long time, she awaited your return with a sarcastic comment.

Life became very dreary, until a strange thing happened. Miss Daker came to gran's cottage. As usual, I was sitting, quietly, in the chimley-corner, in the shadows cast by the oil-lamp.

At first, I thought she'd come about me. She knew my name wasn't Williams, now – and I waited, breathless, for the harsh voice of criticism.

Only it wasn't like that at all. It was quite a different voice, almost human.

"I've come about a new dress, Mrs. Wilshire." Gran was village dressmaker.

"Come in, Frances, my dear. Sit down. What sort of dress, d'ee fancy?"

"I hadn't thought."

Gran gave her a book of patterns and asked about her family. It had never occurred to me that Miss Daker could have a Christian-name or a family. Her father had had a stroke, it seemed, and Miss Daker had to do everything for him. Gran said she was sorry, and spoke about the past. Suddenly, Miss Daker began to cry.

"There, there!" gran said. "Don't take on, so; you've always been so brave about it."

"It would have been different," Miss Daker sobbed, "if only he had come back."

Gran nodded, and blew her nose. It was cruel on those who'd lost a loved one, she said, I knew that her own son, my uncle Harry, was killed in the war.

They talked away, about the war, the Great War, and I realised that they knew each other well. It seemed extraordinary that Miss Daker could be subject to the same weaknesses as other people, but she was – she had loved, and lost – her young man had been killed, and she had never forgotten him.

"I couldn't marry anyone else," she said.

Gran shook her head.

"You should have, Frances. If we can't have exactly what we want, in this life, we've got to make do with second-best."

"Not me, Mrs. Wilshire. It had to be George, or nothing: So it's nothing."

At that point, Miss Daker noticed me. Her face froze.

Realising her astonishment, gran said: "That's my little grandson, Lewis. Our Gilbert's boy. Don't take no notice of 'n. He's as quiet as a mouse. Writing, always writing – I told'n, he'll wear his eyes out."

Miss Daker gave a watery smile. She didn't say I was in her class at school, but she was on her guard from then on. I didn't tell gran she was my teacher, either; but I did ask her if Miss Daker had always been sharp.

"Miss Daker? Oh, you mean Frances! No, she was a good-looking wench, when she was young. Then the war came, and she lost her man, and it've turned her sour. She blames Providence for it, but as I told her, you got to take life as it comes. Poor soul, she've got her cross to bear, and she don't get much chance to talk to anybody about it. She's very proud, you know."

That was on a Saturday. Monday morning came, and my heart sank at the idea of school. I wondered if she'd make me suffer for seeing her undressed, as it were. I was in for a shock. She actually *smiled* at me. Praised my work, patted my head, called me Lewis.

When she made me monitor, it seemed ominous.

That meant I had to collect up the text-books and stow them away in the cupboard. The rest of the class had gone home. We were alone.

"Lewis," she said.

I went up to her desk.

"I don't want to say this," she said, "but if I don't, it'll torment me. I've been thinking, all this week-end, and I've realised something. I've been cruel, a wicked woman. Don't ask me why, because I don't know. But I'm going to say I'm sorry, and ask you not to tell anyone else, ever."

"Yes, Miss Daker. I promise."

And then she did a peculiar thing. She reached out, and pulled me to her, and wept. It was most embarrassing. Uncomfortable, too; she was that bony.

After a few long minutes, she let me go, and I've never told anybody about it, from that day to this.

The other kids couldn't understand the change in her. It wasn't just that she was decent to me. She was like it with everyone.

I didn't understand it at the time, but I do, now, of course. Gran's loss was the same as Miss Daker's. You can see for yourself, on the War Memorial up in the park. *George Henry Wilshire*, it reads, way down near the bottom; he was killed in action in 1916. If he'd lived, he would have been my uncle.

And Miss Daker would have been my aunt.

———————

# FASCINATING READING FROM REDCLIFFE

——

Here is a selection of our popular books about Bristol. In all, there are over 60 titles now in print covering Bristol, Bath and the West Country. A full catalogue is available from the publishers, or go and see the range in your local bookshop.

**Bristol Between the Wars**
*Ed. David Harrison*

Bristol has never seen such years of change as those between the two World Wars, changes mirrored in this compelling account. Chapters on industry, women, sport, architecture, travel, education and more show how these years established the pattern for the city seen today.

This frank, intimate book, richly illustrated with rare, archive photographs, captures a permanent record of a period rapidly slipping beyond personal experience.

"The book that nobody brought up in the 1920s and 1930s will wish to miss . . . excellent value"
*Glos & Avon Life*

**£3.50**

## A City and its Cinemas
*Charles Anderson*

The Rise and Fall of Bristol's picture houses. The author draws on the personal reminiscences of local people who, as patrons or staff, remember the heady days when the shuffling queues were an essential part of a Saturday evening out.

Full of anecdotes about Bristol's 61 cinemas and their often colourful promoters.

"Generously illustrated, shamelessly nostalgic and excellently researched . . . a marvellous picture of mass entertainment in the pre-TV age" *Evening Post*

**£2.95**

## Bristol Blitz Diary
*John Dike*

The chance discovery of a faded old memorandum book has provided a fascinating insight into the German air raids on the city of Bristol.

The diary provides us with a minute-by-minute, bomb-by-bomb, street-by-street, account illustrated with many photographs, several of which are previously unpublished.

**£2.95**

## The Bristol House
*Keith Mallory*

A survey of the development of domestic architecture in the Bristol area. Chapters on medieval buildings, the rise of the Georgian terrace, Victorian villas and artisan terraces, the Edwardian era, the modernist movement and contemporary design. Lavishly illustrated.

**£6.50**

## Tales from the Waterfront
*Peter Nichols*

Six gripping short stories based on the author's personal experience of life and work in the famous Charles Hill dockyard in the late 40s and early 50s. A pungent taste of the harsh realities of 'dock-life' in the past.

**£1.50**